TRENDS IN FOOD TECHNOLOGY

Food and Consumers

Hazel King

www.heinemann.co.uk/library
Visit our website to find out more information about Heinemann Library books.

To order:

☎ Phone 44 (0) 1865 888066

▤ Send a fax to 44 (0) 1865 314091

▣ Visit the Heinemann Bookshop at www.heinemann.co.uk/library to browse our catalogue and order online.

Heinemann Library is an imprint of Pearson Education Limited, a company incorporated in England and Wales having its registered office at Edinburgh Gate, Harlow, Essex, CM20 2JE – Registered company number: 00872828

Edited by Andrew Farrow and Claire Throp
Designed by Richard Parker and Q2A
Illustrated by Art Construction and Big Top (p. 15)
Picture research by Hannah Taylor
Production by Alison Parsons
Originated by Heinemann Library
Printed in China by CTPS

ISBN 978 0 431 14056 8 (hardback)
12 11 10 09 08
10 9 8 7 6 5 4 3 2 1

ISBN 978 0 431 14063 6 (paperback)
12 11 10 09 08
10 9 8 7 6 5 4 3 2 1

British Library Cataloguing in Publication Data
King, Hazel
Food and consumers. – 2nd ed. – (Trends in food technology)
664
A full catalogue record for this book is available from the British Library.

Acknowledgements
We would like to thank the following for permission to reproduce photographs:
© Alamy/Tom Fiddick p. **35 (t)**; © Corbis/zefa/Charles Gullung p. **16**; ENCAMS p. **35 (r)**; © Getty Images/Mark Mainz p. **21**; © Getty Images/Stock Market pp. **17, 29, 34.** © Network Photographers p. **23;** © Pearson Education Ltd/Gareth Boden pp. **6, 11, 12, 18, 19, 25, 31, 32, 33, 40, 41**; © Pearson Education Ltd/Tudor Photography pp. **7, 27, 37;** © Rex Features p. **8**; © Rex Features/Alex Segre p. **42;** © Robert Harding Picture Library p. **5**; © Science Photo Library/James King-Holmes p. **13**.

Cover photograph of a woman in a supermarket reproduced with permission of © Photolibrary/Digital Vision.

We would like to thank Alison Winson for her invaluable help in the preparation of the first edition of this book.

Every effort has been made to contact copyright holders of material reproduced in this book. Any omissions will be rectified in subsequent printings if notice is given to the publishers.

Contents

Shopping for food 4

Introducing consumers 6

Types of consumer 8

Meatless meals 10

Allergic reactions 12

Diabetic diets 14

Multi-cultural matters 16

From sandwich to sushi 18

Too much, too little 20

Addicted to food 22

Healthy messages 24

Healthy eats 26

Young needs 28

Developing the technology 30

Packing food 32

Packaging materials 34

MAP 36

Food labels 38

Kellogg's packaging – case study 40

New developments 42

Resources 44

Glossary 46

Index 48

Any words appearing in the text in bold, **like this**, are explained in the glossary.

Shopping for food

Open all hours

Buying food has never been easier. Our shops are bigger and contain a wider variety of goods than ever before. We also have more options when it comes to paying for food. But more importantly, many of us can buy food at almost any time of the day or night. If you fancy a tub of ice cream at 4 am just call into your local 24-hour supermarket and take your pick.

Over the last 15 years there have been tremendous changes in the way food shops have been owned and run. Before the advent of supermarkets, small businesses, in the form of greengrocers, fishmongers, bakers and so on, would provide customers with specialist goods. Today, a large proportion of the food retail market is owned by just a few major companies, not necessarily based in the United Kingdom, and these provide us with an enormous range of goods, all under one roof. Food shopping has moved from corner shop to superstore.

The introduction of supermarkets owned by large companies has often meant that food prices have come down while the quality of food on offer has improved. The sheer size of many supermarkets enables them to run very efficient businesses with well-trained staff and highly technical equipment. They are also able to negotiate good prices for food products because they order in such large quantities. Food is distributed quickly and easily, giving consumers the choice of a wide range of fresh goods from all over the world. Powerful marketing techniques, such as customer loyalty cards, have also helped supermarkets win customers away from smaller food shops.

Customer loyalty cards are used to gain points that can be exchanged for reductions off future payments or for the purchase of other goods or services.

Out-of-town

The main advantage of an out-of-town supermarket or superstore is its convenience. They have their own car parks, which are usually free, with spaces allocated to parents of young children and people with disabilities. For those without transport, a bus service may be offered. Other services available at superstores often include cash machines, dry cleaners, coffee shops, chemists, post offices and even a hairdresser. Staff are usually on hand if a customer requires help with their packing and systems such as 'self-scanning' enable consumers to calculate their bill as they shop. All these innovations have come about because people want a more convenient way to carry out the mundane task of shopping for food.

Paying for food

How we pay for our shopping has also become quicker and easier. Instead of carrying cash many people use debit, credit or store cards to make payments at the supermarket till. These 'chip and pin' cards provide a safer alternative to writing a signature or handing over cash. Most stores also offer a cashback service.

Food shopping is becoming so convenient we don't even have to leave home to do it! Many supermarkets offer services through which credit cards can be used to buy groceries over the phone or the Internet. By trawling through the products available on-screen, an order can

Out-of-town superstores offer consumers the convenience of having a wide range of goods all under one roof.

be placed, paid for and delivered to your door. Your regular shopping list can even be stored ready for future shopping. Although a charge may be levied for these services, many people feel it is worth it for the amount of time saved. In addition, having items delivered actually helps reduce **carbon emissions** by enabling one vehicle to deliver to many households.

Consumer spending

There are many reasons why changes have occurred in our retail world and one of these is the overall rise in our standard of living. Generally speaking, people have more **disposable income** and are spending more money on 'luxury items' such as holidays abroad and leisure activities. However, this increase in consumer spending doesn't usually mean people spend more on food eaten in the home. But the type of food demanded by consumers today is certainly changing. People want a wide variety of convenient and high-quality food products. Advances in technology have also had a significant impact on the foods we buy and the way in which we shop. Not only are many foods processed so that they can have a long shelf-life, but consumers can store foods in a fridge or freezer at home. There is a wide range of frozen foods available, many of which can be cooked from frozen, adding to their convenience. The rise in the number of households with microwaves has led to more microwavable products being consumed than ever before.

Recent technological developments in food packaging, such as **modified atmosphere packaging (MAP)**, have also enabled products to be preserved for longer. Containers can often be used both for cooking and serving food products such as ready-meals.

Introducing consumers

Consumer power

The type of foods available today reflects the foods demanded by a majority of consumers. Demands tend to echo people's lifestyles. Generally, people are busier and want to spend more time on leisure activities than on household chores such as shopping and cooking. Consumers now demand more convenience-type foods and the food industry has responded accordingly. This has involved input from product development, materials and packaging, production engineering, marketing and manufacturing.

The criteria people tend to judge food by when shopping today veers towards quality, convenience and choice. In the past, people often quoted price as an important factor in decision making about food. However, nowadays, if time is short, consumers may be prepared to spend a little more money in order to have a product that is convenient. A consumer may be aware that the cost of fruit and vegetables is lower at the town's market. However, it may be less convenient and more time consuming to take a separate trip into town (where parking may be difficult or expensive) to buy groceries when a whole array of goods can be purchased together at a supermarket.

Of course, although there are trends towards shopping in large stores and buying food in bulk, this does not mean all consumers follow them. People have different needs and wants. There is a current trend towards choosing locally grown, organic foods, for example, and also those that have not been **genetically modified**.

Food on the move

As well as having a better standard of living, society now enjoys more leisure time. This time is generally due to the advances in technology that help to make household tasks quicker and easier. More of us own automatic washing machines, vacuum cleaners, dish washers, tumble driers, microwave ovens and freezers. Cars make it easier for us to attend leisure time activities such as sports, hobbies and evening classes, or take weekend breaks.

There is a tendency for people to have busy, hurried lifestyles and eating on the move, or 'grazing' rather than sitting down to a meal. Traditionally, most families would sit round a table for breakfast. Lunch would probably be eaten at work or school but the day would end together with an evening meal. Now it is far more likely that breakfast is eaten while running for the bus and tea is consumed at different times during the evening, possibly in

An increasing number of consumers are now choosing to buy organic foods.

Consumers are becoming increasingly concerned about the impact food production is having on the environment.

front of the television or computer. Food products suitable for this lifestyle of grazing include products such as breakfast bars, salads supplied with a spoon, ready-made sandwiches and filled tortilla snacks.

Seasonal food

To meet the many demands of today's consumer, the food industry offers a huge range of products, which provides customers with an incredible choice. In addition, improved transportation and distribution methods mean that foods from all over the world can be purchased from the local supermarket. Without efficient **importation systems** we would not be able to try fruits such as apricots from Turkey, grapefruits from Israel or mangoes from South Africa.

In addition, we are able to eat certain foods all year round. For example, redcurrants are grown in the UK only during the summer months but, by importing them from other countries, UK supermarkets are able to offer them at any time of the year (albeit for a higher price than UK redcurrants sold in July). There is now growing concern about not only losing the value of 'seasonality' (eating foods according to the season in which they are naturally grown) but the impact of such importation on our environment.

Fairtrade foods

Fairtrade food schemes have come about following the exploitation of some workers in developing countries, who receive extremely poor wages in return for goods sold for a sizeable profit by the manufacturers. The Fairtrade mark is a consumer label that guarantees a better deal for producers in developing countries. An example is the Divine Fairtrade chocolate bar.

Types of consumer

Consumer groups

Different types of consumer have emerged over the last decade or so. These pages look at those consumers and the demands they make on today's food industry.

Women

At one time women carried out the majority of food shopping and cooking. Now men are just as likely to shop and cook. This is mainly due to the increased number of women who are working and remaining in work after having children. For example, in 2006 the average number of dependent children per household was just 1.8. The 'average' woman also tends to wait longer before having children; in 2005 the average age for a mother having her first child was 27.3 years, which is 3 years older than in 1971. Since 1992, women aged from 30 to 34 are more likely to give birth than women aged 20 to 24. Household chores have become more of a shared occupation for men and women, so food manufacturers can no longer specifically target women when promoting meals for the family.

Single households

There has also been a significant increase in the number of people living on their own over the last ten years. Today, around 30 per cent of households have one person living on their own, as compared with 14 per cent in 1961. Naturally, this has created a whole new **consumer target group** for food manufacturers. Ready-meals-for-one are aimed at busy working people who haven't the time (or perhaps the inclination) to prepare a meal when they get in from work.

Food manufacturers constantly monitor the type of food bought by different consumers. This allows them to meet the needs of the various consumer groups.

Older people

One reason why the number of single households has increased is because people are living longer. Today, the average man lives to 76 years while the average woman lives to be 80. However, in 1911 men could expect to live to about 49 years, while women lived until they were 52. Our society is now said to have an 'ageing population', which means we have a greater number of older people in comparison with younger generations. This older group of consumers has different needs and wants from younger people so the food industry has had to respond accordingly. More single portion meals are now available, particularly of traditional foods such as steamed pudding and shepherd's pie.

Young people

At the other end of the scale, there is a trend for young people to move out of the family home and into a place of their own at an earlier age. In the past, people tended to wait until marriage before leaving home but now young people often want early independence and choose to wait until they are older before getting married, if they decide to marry at all.

Within this consumer target group there has been a decline in the consumption of red meat, especially amongst females. Attitudes towards vegetarianism appear to have changed; vegetarian food has become more acceptable and is much more readily available. This may be partly explained by the growing multi-cultural society and many religions that involve a vegetarian diet. For example, most Rastafarians and Hindus do not eat meat, while Sikhs will not eat beef and Muslims avoid pork.

Children

Although children have not always been seen in terms of a 'consumer group', they are certainly viewed that way today. There is growing concern about the way children are the target in advertisements for foods that are high in sugar, salt and fat. Many people now believe advertising such foods during children's television time should be banned.

As young children are not able to judge the nutritional value of foods, they tend to choose food by its appearance and taste. Very often children prefer sweets and snacks, which do not necessarily provide them with the necessary nutrients for their growing bodies. When faced with sweets near the checkout counter or advertisements for the latest salty snack, children are bound to put pressure on their parents to buy them.

Children's Food Campaign

The Children's Food Campaign has been set up to help improve young people's health and well-being. The campaign wants:

- better food in schools, including the promotion of fruit and vegetables and the reduction in the availability of unhealthy food
- to protect children from junk food advertising. They want a ban on junk food advertising until after 9 pm
- every child to be taught about healthy food and cookery in school
- clear food labelling that is easy for everyone to understand, including children.

See the website:
www.childrensfoodcampaign.org.uk

Meatless meals

Being vegetarian

Following a vegetarian diet has become increasingly popular but the food eaten by vegetarians can vary enormously. In order to classify the differences within this particular consumer group, categories of vegetarian are used, as outlined in the chart below. However, a growing number of consumers do not fit neatly into a category and may just choose to cut out certain foods from their diet. The food industry realises there is a growing number of 'meat reducers' who contribute to today's vegetarian market.

Why vegetarianism?

Many people believe a diet free from animal products is healthier and give this as their reason for becoming vegetarian. Foods such as meat, butter and cheese contain **saturated fats**, which are thought to contribute to the risk of **coronary heart disease**. Foods that may be found in the diet of a vegetarian are usually low in fat and high in dietary fibre called **non-starch polysaccharide (NSP)**. These include vegetables, wholegrain rice, pulses and **textured vegetable protein (TVP)**. However, vegetarians still need to have a balanced and varied diet for it to be a healthy one.

Concern over food safety has also contributed to a reduction in the consumption of some animal products. Scares such as bovine spongiform encephalopathy (BSE), 'avian flu', *Salmonella* and *E.coli 0157* have convinced many consumers that it is safer to avoid certain foods.

Family tradition or religious belief may also be reasons for becoming vegetarian. Then there are those who do not like the taste, aroma, texture and/or appearance of meat. Economy is also given as a reason for vegetarianism. Many vegetarians believe the rearing of animals is an expensive way to feed the

Classifying vegetarians

Non-meat eaters	Follow a less restricted diet than other vegetarians. Some exclude all types of meat while others cut out only red meat.
Lacto-ovo vegetarian	Do not eat meat, fish or poultry and avoid any ingredients derived from these sources (such as gelatine). They will eat eggs and dairy products.
Lacto vegetarian	Do not eat meat, fish, poultry or eggs and avoid any ingredients derived from these sources. They will eat dairy products.
Vegan	Very strict vegetarians who will not eat any animal product or food derived from animal sources. They also exclude foods and products that involve the use of or the harming of animals (such as leather clothes and shoes).

Vegetarians can obtain sufficient protein from a diet that includes nuts, pulses, soya milk and tofu.

population and that land could be put to better use if plants were grown instead of grazing animals. Some people choose a vegetarian diet because they do not believe in killing animals for human consumption. They also feel that animals are exploited by intensive farming methods.

Essential nutrition

To stay healthy we all need to ensure that we are following a nutritionally balanced diet. It is important for vegetarians to include certain nutrients that may be lacking if their diet excludes meat and other animal foods. These nutrients include protein, iron, vitamin B12 and zinc. A vegan's diet may also lack calcium, riboflavin and vitamin D.

Protein

There are millions of different proteins: plant, animal and human. Like all proteins, food proteins are built from 'building blocks' called **amino acids**. Every cell in our body contains protein obtained from the food we eat and it is used throughout life for the growth, repair and

maintenance of our bodies. There are more than twenty types of amino acids, but eight of them are essential in an adult's diet and nine are essential for children. These must be supplied by the foods we eat since they cannot be made in the body. Animal proteins such as meat, fish, eggs and milk contain all the essential amino acids in the right proportion, which is why vegetarians must eat a varied diet that includes protein foods such as pulses, nuts and seeds.

Vegetarian products

Today's food industry has geared itself up to cater for its vegetarian consumers. A wide range of products can be purchased that meet a vegetarian's nutritional needs and many of these make use of **novel proteins** such as soya, myco-proteins (for example Quorn™, which is made from a mushroom-like plant) and textured vegetable proteins. These products can be processed in a variety of ways to produce items such as tofu, soya milk and vegetarian ready-meals and snacks.

Allergic reactions

Reacting badly

Over the last two decades there has been a considerable growth of interest in adverse (bad) reactions to food, often called food allergy. In fact, only about 1–2 per cent of the population show an intolerance to food, although it is difficult to obtain accurate figures for the following reasons:

- an almost limitless number of foods and **additives** may cause reactions
- testing is very time consuming and some tests may not be particularly sensitive
- reactions vary between people and these can change over time, especially in children
- reactions to a food or additive may not show immediately.

Foods that have frequently been associated with food allergies include peanuts, wheat, cheese, wine, coffee, milk, eggs, potatoes, fish, oats and tomatoes.

Definitions

Various terms are used to describe allergic reactions to food, such as food intolerance, hypersensitivity and food allergy. Food intolerance and hypersensitivity are general terms for all adverse reactions that occur more than once and do not have **psychological** causes. The term 'food allergy' is used if a reaction is reproducible and involves an abnormal reaction in the immune system, resulting in **pathological** changes in the gut or elsewhere.

Allergic reactions can have an immediate or a delayed response. Symptoms might include redness of the skin, itching, swelling, breathing difficulties and abdominal pain.

The severity of the symptoms varies but can range from mild to life-threatening such as **anaphylactic shock**. Peanuts, almonds, Brazil nuts, hazelnuts and walnuts are the foods most likely to provoke a reaction as well as fish, shellfish, eggs and dairy products. Anyone with a major allergic reaction needs to carry special adrenaline injections that they can administer themselves if necessary to reduce the symptoms.

Coeliac disease

Coeliac disease is a condition that causes the wall of the small intestine to become damaged if gluten is eaten. Gluten is a protein found mainly in wheat but it is also present in rye, barley and oats. It is thought that around one in a thousand people in the UK suffer with coeliac disease. Many others may have an intolerance to gluten, however.

 Anyone with coeliac disease must avoid a wide range of foods that contain gluten (a protein found in wheat, rye, barley and oats).

If the lining of the small intestine becomes damaged, the gut will fail to absorb adequate nutrients from food. As a result, any of the following symptoms may occur: stomach pain, diarrhoea, vomiting, exhaustion, anaemia, bloating, mouth ulcers and weight loss. The only way a coeliac can prevent these symptoms is by avoiding all foods that contain gluten.

Because gluten is present in flour, a common ingredient, a very wide range of foods are involved. They include the majority of biscuits, cakes, pastries and breads, as well as products that have used a starch-based thickener such as many processed meals, desserts and snacks. Beer, too, has to be avoided as it cannot be guaranteed to be free from gluten.

Health food shops

Health food shops have sold products such as bread and cakes for coeliacs for some time but supermarkets and other stores are also beginning to cater for such specialist diets. Labelling is also being used to highlight gluten-free products.

Food additives

With the increase in food processing and manufactured products, additives are playing an increasing role in food production. Some consumer groups are opposed to their use because of the possibility of an adverse reaction. The additives most often mentioned in connection with sensitivity include colouring agents such as tartrazine (E102), found in some soft drinks, and antioxidants such as butylated hydroxytoluene (BHT), present in some margarines, and butylated hydroxyanisole (BHA), found in some soup mixes and cheese spreads.

 Skin prick testing (SPT) uses drops of diluted food to test for food allergies. This method of testing is safe for people of all ages.

Hyperactivity and children

Clearly it is difficult to link an allergy to an additive because they are not usually eaten on their own. However, there is concern that children who eat a lot of processed foods will be consuming a high proportion of additives in relation to body size. Some children suffer from increased activity after eating just a small amount of a food additive. This is known as hyperactivity.

Certain additives, such as the sorbic acid found in some fruit yoghurts, are necessary to ensure that a food is preserved properly and is safe to eat. All additives given an 'E' number have been rigorously tested and are accepted as safe throughout the European Union.

Diabetic diets

Glucose

Glucose is our body's main source of energy. The process of obtaining energy from food is complicated but most of our energy is supplied by carbohydrate foods such as bread, pasta, rice, potatoes and sugar. When all carbohydrates (except **NSP**) are eaten they are broken down during digestion and eventually absorbed as glucose, galactose and fructose. These **monosaccharides** then travel via the bloodstream to the liver (where galactose and fructose are converted to glucose) and the muscles.

The liver and muscles transform glucose into glycogen, which acts as a reserve of carbohydrate for the body and can be converted back into glucose to supply the body with energy. Several hormones control the way in which our body uses glucose. One of these hormones is called insulin. Hormones are chemical messengers produced by one part of the body to cause a response in another part.

Insulin

Unfortunately for some people, the pancreas isn't always able to produce sufficient insulin and as a result the amount of glucose circulating in the blood is unusually large. Also, the liver and muscles fail to use the glucose for conversion to glycogen for energy. This means the body has to use fat and protein instead of carbohydrate foods as its source of energy, which can be harmful. The result is a disease called diabetes mellitus.

Diabetes mellitus

Excessively high or low levels of glucose in the blood are very serious and must be controlled.

Diabetics must be careful about what they eat and some have to take tablets or administer a daily injection of insulin. A diet high in complex carbohydrates and NSP (one containing wholemeal bread, wholegrain rice and cereals, vegetables and fruit) is recommended because these foods help to control the rate at which sugar is absorbed into the blood.

It is unclear exactly why diabetes develops or what causes it, but people with diabetes do not make sufficient insulin in their bodies. There are two types of diabetes: young people's diabetes (or Type 1) and maturity onset diabetes (or Type 2).

Type 1 diabetes usually develops suddenly and the symptoms are severe. It normally occurs before the age of 40 and young people with this type of diabetes often have a **genetic** tendency towards it.

Type 2 diabetes does not require treatment with insulin because usually diabetics still produce some insulin of their own. They can control their diabetes by following healthy eating guidelines. This form tends to affect middle-aged and older people, although people who are overweight are at a higher risk of developing the disease as they get older.

Healthy eating

Of course everyone is encouraged to follow a healthy eating regime and this is equally important for diabetics. The type of diet recommended for diabetics follows current views on healthy eating and so includes reduced fat intake, especially **saturated fat**, reduced salt and sugar intake but increased NSP intake. Of course, it can be difficult to monitor the diet of a young child so it is important that children understand the need to stick to their diet.

A diabetic must ensure that they do not have too much sugar or sugary products, such as sweets, cakes, biscuits and fizzy drinks, which cause a rapid rise in blood sugar levels. However, although the amount needs to be reduced, they do not have to be avoided altogether. Sweet treats can be eaten occasionally, preferably after a meal rather than on an empty stomach. It is now generally thought that products such as diabetic chocolate are not necessary because they are often no lower in fat or **calories** than ordinary chocolate.

Diabetic guidelines

As well as following a healthy diet, diabetics also need to consider how much and how often they eat. It is important to eat regular meals and to avoid skipping meals. They must watch out for hidden fats that are found in pastries, cakes, biscuits and snacks. Alcohol consumption should be kept to a minimum and should not be used to replace meals. Drink must not be consumed on an empty stomach as it lowers blood sugar levels. Weight needs to be monitored to avoid becoming overweight.

 The 'eatwell plate' shows how much of what you eat should come from each food group. This includes everything you eat during the day, including snacks.

Multi-cultural matters

Consumer influence

The consumer is a powerful force behind the development of new food products. If the majority of consumers started showing concern about their salt intake, then manufacturers would gradually reduce the levels of salt in processed foods. This is equally true when it comes to meeting the needs of different consumer groups. For example, 'meals for one' have helped to fill a gap in the market for the growing number of adults living on their own. As society has become more multi-cultural, so the demand for foods traditionally from other cultures has increased. In the UK, 7.9 per cent of the population is of ethnic minority origin.

Multi-cultural societies

All cultures have customs with which they are traditionally associated, although not all members of that culture necessarily follow them. Dietary customs are often associated with religious beliefs such as the Christian tradition of eating pancakes on Shrove Tuesday (the day before Lent). During the **fasting** of Lent, eggs are forbidden so they are used up in the pancake batter. Ramadan takes place during the ninth month of the Muslim year. Muslims are expected to fast during daylight hours of this month.

In the Asian community there are many regional and religious variations, but generally **staple** foods include chapattis (Indian unleavened bread) and rice. Pulses are used quite extensively, especially by vegetarians, for example in dahl (an Indian dish made from lentils). Muslims do not eat pork and all meat must be halal, which means it has been slaughtered according to Muslim law by a halal butcher. Hindus and Sikhs do not eat beef or drink alcohol. Many Hindus are vegetarian as they are against violence and, for them, the cow is sacred.

Within the Jewish community, meat must be kosher, which means it is slaughtered according to Jewish law. Followers of Judaism do not eat pork or shellfish.

 In the UK there is growing interest in foods from other cultures. People are more receptive to different ingredients, flavours, aromas and methods of cooking.

Also, a three-hour gap must pass between eating meat and dairy products and even the preparation of these foods must take place separately, so different sinks and equipment are required.

The diet of the Afro-Caribbean community is often based on rice and maize (corn) as well as vegetables such as yams, sweet potatoes and plantains. These foods all have a high starch content, so form the staple diet. Both meat and fish are eaten, although Rastafarians are vegetarian and avoid all processed and preserved foods as well as dairy products, eggs, salt and alcohol.

Further afield

Of course, the demand for foods with a multi-cultural feel does not just come from people who have their roots in another culture. Generally, people are travelling more than ever before and are visiting a wider variety of countries. By visiting countries and getting a taste of another culture, people later want to replicate those dishes for themselves at home or buy them in a restaurant or shop. This has resulted in an increase in the variety of restaurants as well as the range of food products on sale. People are also more receptive to new ideas and are prepared to try dishes from other countries.

Methods of cooking

Along with an interest in different ingredients, flavours and aromas, new dishes introduce the opportunity for new methods of cooking. Indian cuisine uses the tandoor oven, oriental food is cooked in a wok, a tagine is used in Moroccan cookery and barbecued food is popular in hot climates such as in Australia.

 Barbecued food is popular in hot climates such as Australia.

In fact, despite the unpredictability of the weather, barbecues are becoming increasingly trendy in cooler climates such as in Western Europe, and not just to entertain the family at weekends. Chef Nigel Tunnicliff's company Blistering Barbecues provides al fresco catering by mixing traditional open fire cooking with up-to-date barbecue equipment.

Project

Investigate the range of products that are currently marketed for barbecue cooking. As a vegetarian company, your task is to design a range of three barbecue products that would appeal to consumers who do not eat meat. Plan the packaging for each product and include the name of your company.

From sandwich to sushi

Fast food

When you think of fast food you don't necessarily think of a sandwich, although sandwiches are both quick to prepare and easy to eat. Like all fast food, you don't have to go to the trouble of making sandwiches yourself as they can now be purchased in all sorts of retail outlets, from supermarkets to petrol stations. In fact, sandwiches are now the most popular convenience food. Consumers spend more on ready-made sandwiches than any other fast food. The British sandwich market was worth £2.8 billion in 2006.

The sandwich is thought to have been invented by the 4th Earl of Sandwich in the 18th century. If the Earl had chosen to use one of the many titles he was offered, we could have been eating a 'Portsmouth' today! According to the British Sandwich Association, there are approximately 2 million sandwiches purchased outside the home every year in the UK alone (this figure includes all bread-filled snacks such as pitas and rolls). In fact, the sandwich industry is so big in the UK that it provides full- and part-time employment for over 300,000 people.

Varieties of sandwich

Sandwiches are perfect when it comes to refuelling during a hectic lunchtime. They are easily transportable and can contain a variety of different fillings; they also satisfy the appetite quickly and can be relatively nutritious. Of course, consumer demand has led to many variations on the original theme. For example, the bread may be wholewheat, wholegrain, rye or granary, it may be flavoured with cheese or coloured with the addition of red pepper or tomato. Fillings have become both adventurous, such as Wensleydale cheese and watercress with carrot chutney, and decidedly challenging, such as sausage and egg in baked bean bread!

A further expansion of the sandwich has been the introduction of items such as tortilla wraps and filled Italian ciabatta bread. While these may be slightly more expensive than the average sandwich, it would appear that although people have less time for eating they are often prepared to spend a little more on the food they consume. The convenience of

 The 4th Earl of Sandwich would be impressed: the British sandwich market is worth more than the pizza and burger markets.

prepacked food is also tempting, especially when an entire packed lunch can be picked up at the local shop. Sandwiches are teamed up with crisps, a drink and perhaps a piece of fruit or yoghurt for a complete lunchtime experience without any effort.

Bagels

Another popular bread-based lunchtime snack is the bagel. Originally from the United States, the bagel looks a bit like a doughnut without the sugar coating and has a denser texture. One of the bagel's selling points is that it is low in fat (although the nutritional information shows this doesn't necessarily mean it is low in **calories**). Bagels are available in a variety of sweet and savoury flavours, in addition to the plain version. They can be eaten hot or cold, filled or unfilled. After toasting they may be spread with all kinds of fillings from soft cheese to peanut butter.

According to a bagel company called Oi! Bagel, the most popular fillings with their customers include smoked salmon and cream cheese in first place, followed closely by pastrami and Swiss bagel, then turkey and bacon club. The bagels themselves can be topped with sesame seeds or poppy seeds or flavoured with onions.

Sushi

The latest competition to sandwiches is sushi, a Japanese dish containing rice and sushi vinegar. These oriental snacks have now found their way out of restaurants or sushi bars and onto the high street as an exciting new lunchtime snack.

Sushi comes in bite-sized pieces and, in addition to cooked rice, can contain fish, seafood, egg and nori seaweed. The ingredients are carefully layered, then rolled up before being sliced and up-ended, ready to be served.

Although sushi can be manufactured quite easily these days, in Japan it traditionally took a chef about ten years to learn the art of sushi-making. The slicing of the raw ingredients requires a great deal of knife skill and the quantity of each ingredient must be precisely judged in order to obtain the perfect result. The sushi is traditionally rolled on bamboo mats and requires just the right amount of pressure.

 Japanese sushi is now a popular lunch-time snack.

Too much, too little

Food as fuel

Eating should be fun but for many people food can cause unnecessary suffering. This may be because a poor diet has led to health problems in later life or it may be that food is eaten, or avoided, for emotional rather than physical reasons.

Food is a fuel and that is how most animals would view it. However, for humans, food comes from a wide variety of sources which can be combined and cooked in numerous ways, making eating much more interesting than a simple refuelling process. Also, because humans are complex and sociable beings, in addition to our physical well-being, eating can affect our **psychological** and emotional state.

Anorexia nervosa

Anorexia nervosa is a disorder that makes people obsessively anxious about their body weight. The name is in fact confusing because 'anorexia' literally means 'loss of appetite' but people with anorexia nervosa do not lose their appetite. Instead, they become so frightened of gaining weight that they eat as little as possible. It is thought that anorexia affects about 1 per cent of women between the ages of 15 and 30 in the UK. However, a small number of young men are also affected and anorexia nervosa is becoming an increasing problem in girls under 15.

Many people believe the media and fashion industries contribute to the high incidence of anorexia nervosa in the Western world. For many years the way women have been portrayed by these industries has been as someone who is very slim. These images can influence teenage girls, whose bodies are changing as they develop into women. Many girls feel they must diet in order to maintain or achieve a slim figure but this may well be to the detriment of their health. Fortunately there is now a slight move by the media towards using models with more realistic proportions.

For the anorexic, the fear of fatness goes far beyond a simple desire to be slim. For them, the need to make themselves thinner dominates all other emotions. Even when they are very underweight they may still see themselves as fat. This distorted perception of how they look is characteristic of the disorder. Anorexics feel that their value as a person is directly affected by their body shape.

Bulimia nervosa

Bulimia nervosa is also a disorder whereby someone is unable to relate normally to food, but in this case they do not generally have the dramatic weight loss associated with anorexia nervosa. A bulimic usually swings between bingeing and an urgent desire to get rid of everything that has been consumed. The bingeing of food is almost always carried out in secret and may involve eating absolutely anything that is available and edible (although uncooked foods may also be chosen as part of the binge). After eating such a large amount, someone with bulimia nervosa will then panic and need to rid their body of everything they have consumed. This may be done by making themselves vomit or they may take laxatives (to stimulate the bowels) or diuretics (to increase the excretion of urine), or even use all three. Alternatively, excessive **fasting** or exercise may be undertaken to compensate for the high **calorie** intake.

Initially, someone with bulimia nervosa may feel they have found a way to control their lives because they can eat whatever they like without putting on any weight. However, in reality it is the bulimia nervosa that actually has the control and dictates the way in which a person lives their life. Just like anorexia nervosa, the incidence of bulimia is more common among women and both conditions can have serious medical consequences, as shown below.

Anorexia nervosa

- Poor circulation
- Low blood pressure
- Brittle bones
- Increased facial hair
- Loss of periods/infertility
- Fainting and dizziness
- Hair loss
- Dehydration
- Kidney damage.

Bulimia nervosa

- Tooth decay
- Irregular periods
- Damage to the bowel
- Constipation
- Heart and kidney disease
- Intestinal damage
- Puffiness of face and fingers
- Increased hair growth on face and body
- Mineral imbalances in the body.

Endorphin boost

The American Nobel prize-winning scientist, James Watson, has a different theory about body size. Instead of seeing thinness as something to desire, he suggests that a lack of body fat can make people discontent. After studying body chemicals, he believes that extra body fat leads to a boost of endorphins, the natural mood-enhancing chemical. The more fat, the more endorphins and so the more content a person feels.

Ultra-slim stars such as Nicole Richie provide teenage girls with a role model.

Addicted to food

Obesity

In 1999 the UK government laid down targets for improving the nation's health. One of these targets was to reduce the incidence of **coronary heart disease**. One of the many **risk factors** known to increase a person's chance of developing coronary heart disease is obesity.

Obesity officially became a disease around 50 years ago when it entered the International Classification of Diseases. It can be defined according to a body mass index (BMI). A person's BMI is calculated by dividing their weight in kilograms (kg) by their height in metres squared (m^2). The resulting figure can then be checked against the following BMI categories:

BMI	Grade
<20	Underweight
20–25	Normal weight
25–30	Overweight
>30	Obese

Knowledge of this system is important for those concerned about their health because, in general, risks begin to increase when the BMI is above 25. The risks increase even more rapidly when a BMI of over 30 is reached. However, care must be taken when using such a system as it does not take account of the components of body weight. Muscle, for example, is heavier than fat, so a trained athlete may be classified as obese despite having very little body fat!

Fat versus lean

The amount of body fat is an important aspect of health, particularly in relation to coronary heart disease. For women, the proportion of fat on their body tends to be higher than that of men, due to their reproductive role and hormone activity. As a guide, an adult woman should have between 25 and 28 per cent body fat whereas an adult male should have 15 per cent.

The high fat content of the typical Western diet is partly responsible for the increase in body fat levels over the last decade. People tend to snack rather than eat whole meals, relying on fast foods such as takeaways. A high proportion of these foods, such as chips, burgers, fried chicken and doughnuts, are fried or contain a great deal of fat. The UK now has the largest fast-food and take-away market in Europe.

However, the food industry can't be entirely to blame for an increase in obesity, after all, the industry claims to only give consumers what they want. Other lifestyle habits that are likely to contribute include spending more time sitting down and lack of exercise. Occupations are generally less physical than they used to be and more people travel by car, even for short journeys. Fewer children walk to and from school and the increase in home computers has meant that it is not just a television screen that captivates young and old alike during the evenings.

The consequences of becoming overweight make grim reading. Statistics show that obese people are both more likely to die prematurely and more likely to develop diabetes.

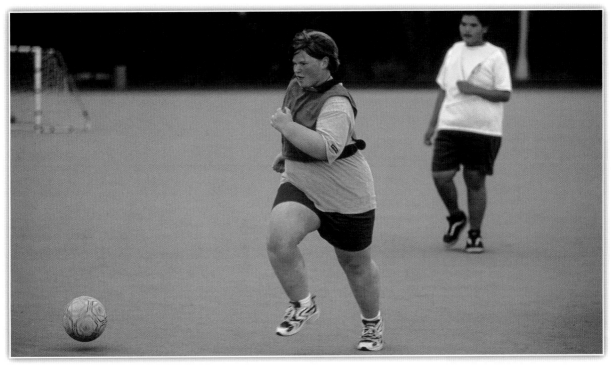

Slimming down

The amount of people with excess weight today makes little sense when supermarket shelves are packed with low-fat, reduced **calorie** foods and drinks. Despite these products, and the medical evidence stating the consequences of obesity, it remains exceedingly difficult for people to lose weight. A person really has to want to reduce the amount they eat in order to achieve a significant difference in their weight. Slimming clubs and classes are usually very helpful, mainly due to the support offered by other people. Also, foods are often classified, perhaps using a points system, so it is easier to decide what to eat, how much and how often.

Any diet offering a great deal of weight loss in a short period of time must be regarded with caution. It is likely that any weight lost will go straight back on after the diet has stopped. Diets like these cannot be followed long term because they do not supply all the necessary nutrients. For serious obesity (BMI of 40+), surgery may be an option if all else has failed. This can involve stapling the stomach so that

 A diet high in fat contributes to today's obesity problem. Reducing calorie intake and exercising can help.

Fat cats

Unfortunately, it is not just people who are being classified as obese. The results of a survey published in 2007 showed that over half the UK's 7 million dogs and a fifth of its 9.5 million cats are estimated to be overweight. Dog and cat owners are putting their pet's health at risk by allowing their pet to become overweight.

only small amounts of food can be eaten. Food supplements are likely to be needed afterwards and plastic surgery may be necessary to remove surplus folds of skin after the weight has been lost. This really is a last resort.

Healthy messages

Food or nutrient?

Most people do not think about nutrients when they eat food. However, our diet can contribute to the risk of diseases such as **coronary heart disease**. In order to help people choose a diet that contains the foods they need for good health, dietary guidelines have been drawn up by various health organizations. Dietary guidelines do not tell people exactly what to eat because there are many healthy diets. Individuals must choose a diet according to their own lifestyle and preferences.

In the UK, the Government's Food Standards Agency has produced some practical tips to help people make healthier choices (see below). All advice, guidance and information about healthy eating and nutrition can be found on their 'eatwell' website along with the eatwell plate (see page 15).

Eat well, be well

There is a great deal of information reported about foods and their effect on health.

Eight tips for eating well

1. Base your meals on starchy foods.
2. Eat lots of fruit and vegetables.
3. Eat more fish.
4. Cut down on saturated fat and sugar
5. Try to eat less salt – no more than 6 grams a day.
6. Get active and try to be a healthy weight.
7. Drink plenty of water.
8. Don't miss breakfast.

Sometimes advice can appear confusing, so the Food Standards Agency has provided clear, easy-to-access information using the theme 'eat well, be well'. Their website uses the following headings to categorise information:

- Healthy diet
- Ages and stages
- Health issues
- Keeping food safe
- Food labels.

In fact, the types of food we are being advised to eat now are very similar to recommendations in previous years. However, now there is perhaps greater concern about the health of the nation, and children in particular. The eatwell plate continues to reinforce the need for everyone to eat at least five portions of fruit and vegetables every day.

DRVs

In 1991 a British government committee, called the Committee on Medical Aspects of Food Policy (COMA), published a report entitled 'Dietary Reference Values'. It contained details of the amounts of the various nutrients we need to consume. The report provided details of the range of nutrient requirements likely to be found in the UK population. A very wide range of vitamins and minerals were included and recommendations for the amount of fat, carbohydrate and **non-starch polysaccharide (NSP)** were also included.

The Dietary Reference Values (DRVs) can be used for the following purposes:

- to assess the adequacy of diets of individuals and groups of people
- to calculate the nutritional content of meals and menus
- to plan food supplies.

Try to eat at least five portions of a variety of fruit and vegetables every day. It might be easier than you think!

DRVs for the energy-providing nutrients

- Fat should supply 35% of total energy, with no more than 11% coming from **saturated fat.**
- Protein should supply 15% of total energy.
- Carbohydrate should supply 50% of total energy (39% from starch, 11% from non-milk extrinsic sugar, i.e. all types of sugar, syrup and honey).

However, the DRV report was not very 'user friendly' for the general public. Information on the 'eatwell' website is much clearer to follow.

The Scientific Advisory Committee on Nutrition (SACN) has now replaced COMA. They are currently in the process of reviewing the UK's nutritional requirements through the Energy Requirements Working Group.

Government guidelines

In 1999 the British government published a white paper concerned with the nation's health. The government declared that 'good health, like good education, should be within reach of all'. The white paper, entitled 'Saving Lives: Our Healthier Nation', remains in force until 2010. Its two goals are:

- to improve the health of the population as a whole by increasing the length of people's lives and the number of years people spend free from illness
- to improve the health of those with a low income and to narrow the health gap.

These goals are consistent with the aims of both the World Health Organization and the European Union (EU).

Healthy eats

Healthy choice

The international high street store Marks and Spencer now offers a range of healthy foods that it feels reinforces and supports the Government's 'eatwell' guidance. The food range, also called Eat Well, is free from artificial colours, flavours, sweeteners and hydrogenated fats. The Marks and Spencer Eat Well range follows the premise that people know they should follow a healthy diet but working out what should or should not be eaten is not always straightforward, so they have worked it out instead.

Healthy sunflowers

Marks and Spencer label their Eat Well range with a bright yellow sunflower and emphasise three healthy eating tips:

1   Eat a balanced diet.
2   Eat less saturated fat.
3   Don't eat as much salt.

Their website and Eat Well magazine provides a more detailed explanation to back up their healthy eating guidance.

Healthy all week

In order to appeal to a wide variety of customers, Marks and Spencer have had to develop a broad range of products. Their marketing emphasises the choice that is on offer from more than 1,300 foods and drinks. Items are available for breakfast, lunch, dinner, dessert and snack so their aim is to provide healthy, balanced products that will meet the needs of different consumers at various times of the day.

Marks and Spencer show how easy it can be to follow a healthy diet. A seven-day guide is even provided, offering suggested meals for one week with the nutritional values calculated at the end of each day.

Eat the rainbow

For some time now dietary advice has included eating five portions of fruit and vegetables every day. Marks and Spencer have highlighted this aspect by referring to the colours of a rainbow. By choosing foods that are different colours, it is likely that a variety of nutrients will be included in the diet. For example, by putting lettuce, tomato, orange pepper and onion in a cheese sandwich, a wide range of vitamins and minerals will be present. The Eat Well range includes some rather unusual (as well as colourful) ingredients such as acai berries, edamame beans, acerola cherries and pomegranate.

Product range

These are some of the products available in Marks and Spencer's Eat Well range:
- Raspberry breakfast smoothie
- Cranberry and orange cookies
- Falafel flatbread
- Aromatic duck with jasmine rice
- Spicy meatballs
- Tomato salsa
- 'Very berry' panna cotta.

The Marks and Spencer Eat Well range includes over 1,300 healthily balanced foods and drinks, all free from artificial colours, flavourings, sweeteners and hydrogenated fats.

Healthy help

In order to support consumers in their quest to follow a healthy lifestyle, Marks and Spencer provide services in conjunction with their Eat Well products:

- Health advisors are available in all food stores so if a customer has a question relating to food and nutrition they will be directed to the health advisor.
- A range of fact sheets are provided online or in food stores, offering information on a range of topics such as food allergies and balanced diets.
- Questions related to nutrition will be responded to by the Marks and Spencer nutritionist using their online 'ask the nutritionist'.

Designing for children

Getting young children to eat healthy foods can be very difficult. Imagine you have been asked by another big food producer to develop a range of healthy meals for children between the ages of 5 and 10. Your range must include both sweet and savoury meals and all must include a healthy balance of nutrients. It is important to find out what children like to eat first, so try asking a group of young children about different ingredients. Also, ask them how they like to eat (for example with a fork, spoon or their fingers). Present your ideas as coloured design ideas with explanatory labels and notes.

Young needs

Pregnancy

Evidence provided by studies of pregnant women and their babies has shown that if a woman can adapt her diet (as necessary) before conceiving, then there are fewer health risks for the baby. What a woman eats and drinks three to six months before conception and for the first few weeks of pregnancy is thought to greatly influence the early development of the embryo.

Recommendations include a daily supply of the B vitamin folic acid (known as folate in its natural form), to be taken from the time contraception is stopped until the twelfth week of pregnancy. This is believed to significantly reduce the risk of giving birth to a baby with a congenital neural tube defect such as spina bifida (in which the spine has not developed properly). Foods that contain folate include brussels sprouts, spinach, granary bread, nuts and oranges, as well as various **fortified** breakfast cereals and breads, but daily

supplements of folic acid are recommended because even a healthy diet is unlikely to supply the amount required. (Liver also contains folate, but due to the high levels of vitamin A in liver, women who are pregnant or are thinking of becoming pregnant should avoid liver altogether. This is because high levels of vitamin A have been linked with birth defects.)

Alcohol

An excessive intake of alcohol can lead to birth defects so it should be avoided before conception. The UK government now advises pregnant women and those trying for a baby not to drink alcohol.

Units of alcohol

1 unit of alcohol =

- half a pint of ordinary strength (3.5% ABV) lager/beer/cider
- 1 small glass of wine (9% ABV) Note: many wines are 11 or 12% ABV
- 1 × 25ml measure of spirit (40% ABV)

Planning a menu

By following current dietary guidelines and eating sensible amounts of food, a pregnant woman can achieve a healthy, balanced diet. Towards the end of pregnancy (in the last **trimester**) a woman may need to increase her **calorie** intake by about 200 calories (0.8MJ) per day. Suggest a week's menu for each of the following stages of pregnancy: one month, six months and eight months. Remember to include a variety of foods!

Infants

A human baby is able to survive on milk alone for its first three months. The milk may be breast milk or formula milk specially developed for babies. Once a baby reaches its fourth month it can cope with a rusk or cereal mixed with milk. When it reaches five or six months it can start to bite and chew lumps of food and this is the stage when an increased variety of tastes and textures can be introduced into the diet. The process of introducing foods other than milk to the baby's

It is especially important for pregnant women, women who are breastfeeding, and babies and toddlers, to avoid infection from food. Infants have an immature immune system so cannot fight infection easily. Food should be hygienically prepared and cooked or reheated thoroughly. Ingredients must be fresh and well within their date mark.

diet is known as weaning. If a baby has the same food as the rest of the family (even if mashed or puréed) the food should contain no added salt. This is because a baby's kidneys cannot cope with additional salt. Adults can sprinkle salt on their own meals later or perhaps they will be encouraged to cut down on their own salt intake!

It is also important to help a child develop good dietary habits during its first few years. By not adding sugar to foods and avoiding sugary drinks, a child is less likely to get a taste for sweet things. Even teeth buried beneath the gums can suffer tooth decay. The more varied and interesting food can be made for young children, the more likely they are to be adventurous in their tastes as they grow up.

Young people

After their first year, the growth rate of young children is not as great. It tends to occur in spurts, which are often accompanied by surges of appetite. Activity increases during the second year as a child becomes increasingly mobile but the amount a young child can eat remains small due to a limited capacity. Having a full set of milk teeth by the age of about two also increases the variety of foods they can eat. For both these reasons, healthy snacks between meals are important for additional energy and for a wider range of food experiences.

The National Diet and Nutrition Survey of young people, published in 2000, found that many children were eating large amounts of salt and sugar and insufficient fruit and vegetables. Children were also considered to be having too much saturated fat in their diet. In addition, they were thought to be not doing enough exercise.

Healthy snack ideas for young children

- Sandwiches containing cucumber, savoury spreads, chopped tomato with cheese
- Fresh or dried fruit
- Raw vegetables cut into pieces
- Dry breakfast cereal
- Savoury biscuits
- Yoghurt or milk
- Plain popcorn
- Cheesy scones.

Developing the technology

Kitchen gadgets

At one time, new food-related technological developments were mainly based around the domestic kitchen, with food processors, automatic ovens, electric whisks, fridge-freezers, microwave ovens and so on. Today, new kitchen gadgets, such as the bread-maker, still appear from time to time but the main thrust of new technology has been in the food industry itself.

Towards the end of the 1990s, innovations in food and packaging appeared at a phenomenal rate. Once the microwave oven was well-established in the majority of homes, food technologists were frantically developing products that could be reheated (still in its packaging) within minutes. For example, ready-meals can now be reheated from the chilled, frozen or **ambient** state. Even the traditionally fat-laden chip was given a high-tech 'healthy' image by being packaged in a box ready for a blast of microwaves.

Novel pizza

Of course, developments such as these do not happen overnight. Adequate market research must be carried out to ensure this is what the consumer wants. Also, a new food product must go through a number of tests in order to produce a quality result that meets the relevant food safety requirements. For example, pizzas are now commonplace. The pizza range has been extended by adapting the texture, thickness and flavour of the base. A variety of ingredients are used as toppings and the pizzas have been folded, rolled, divided and shaped in order to produce something different. But, just when the consumer thought nothing new could come from a pizza, along came a pizza that can be cooked from frozen in a toaster without its topping being lost!

Value-added

Products such as the toasted pizza and many other convenience foods have led to the term 'value-added'. This refers to foods that have undergone secondary processing in order to produce ready-to-use products. Consider the difference in effort involved in making a hot rice pudding using ingredients and heating ready-made puddings.

Homemade rice pudding

Method: Place pudding rice in dish with milk, sugar, butter and nutmeg. Bake for 2½ hours, stirring 2–3 times during cooking.

Tinned rice pudding

Method: Empty contents of can into saucepan. Heat gently for 3–4 minutes, stirring frequently.

Ambient rice pudding

Method: Remove all foil. Heat on full power (650W microwave) for 50 seconds, stirring halfway through heating time.

Functional foods

As well as demanding high-quality foods that require little effort at home, today's consumer also wants 'healthy' products. Definitions of healthy are likely to vary depending on whether you are talking to a consumer, a manufacturer or a nutritionist, but nevertheless, a vast array of products have some sort of health label.

These products are referred to as 'value-added' because they have undergone secondary processing that provides the consumer with a ready-to-use product.

Once again, technology has played a significant role in the development of foods that are acceptable to consumers and yet are low in fat, sugar or salt, or high in **NSP**. Foods that claim to have specific health benefits are often referred to as functional foods or **smart foods**. Any food that makes a specific health claim should obtain a licence under the Medicines Act, so it is wise for a consumer to check this out before relying on the claim. In addition, it is worth reading the nutritional labelling of any product with a health claim. Unlike other foods, a nutritional breakdown is required to be on the label by law.

Benecol®

Benecol® foods are described as functional foods because they claim to lower blood **cholesterol** when eaten as part of a healthy diet. Cholesterol is a fatty substance naturally present in the body. If levels in the blood become too high, the cholesterol can contribute to the 'clogging up' of the arteries which could increase the risk of **coronary heart disease**.

Benecol® products, such as a margarine spread and yoghurt, contain plant stanol **esters**, which occur naturally in plants such as corn, beans and rye. In the 1990s, a Finnish food manufacturer called Raisio, managed to invent and **patent** a process of blending the plant stanols with rapeseed oil to create plant stanol esters. It is believed that when the recommended amount of plant stanol ester is introduced into the diet the amount of cholesterol absorbed from food falls from 50 to 20 per cent. However, it is important to remember that blood cholesterol levels and the body's response to dietary levels also depends on a person's **genetic** make-up.

Packing food

Packing up

Packaging has become big business in the Western world. There are few items of food without at least one layer of wrapping. Even if you do manage to reach the supermarket checkout with a package-free product, the chances are the cashier will put it into a plastic bag for you anyway! This extra packaging does not just result in mountains of waste plastic, paper and cardboard for the consumer, manufacturers are having to shoulder the burden, too. The cost of packaging materials is rising at a higher rate than the food itself. But for the manufacturer, it is worth the investment. Packaging is believed to have a greater influence on food sales than something as important as the quality of the food inside.

 A great deal of packaging is necessary to ensure the safe storage and transportation of goods.

Packaging costs

Food packaging usually ends up in a bin. In fact, packaging makes up about 30 per cent of the UK's domestic waste. Every household adds to the country's 20-million-tonne rubbish mountain by throwing away, on average, a tonne of waste each year. While consumers are paying for all the packaging, it is the environment that is suffering the consequences. It has been estimated that for every £75 spent on groceries, £10 pays for the packaging. For certain products, packaging costs are staggeringly high. For example, a box of breakfast cereal can cost 45 times more than the price a farmer gets for its main ingredient.

The increase in the amount of packaging used today has significant consequences for us and our environment, including:

- extra costs due to the collection and disposal of the extra waste and the subsequent pollution created by that waste

- increased production of materials to meet the demand for packaging, and increased waste products as a result
- loss of natural resources such as trees (paper, cardboard) and oil (plastics).

Recycling

There are many ways in which consumers, retailers and manufacturers can help to reduce the amount of waste generated by food packaging. Many materials are now successfully recycled by being made into new products or by being reused. Recycling bins are located at many supermarkets and household refuse sites. Here, consumers can drop off used plastic bottles, glass bottles, aluminium and steel cans. The materials are then collected by recycling companies or local councils and taken to be cleaned and processed for reuse. There is always more that could be done, of course. In German supermarkets, separate bins are provided next to the checkout so the extra plastic packaging can be removed before the goods are even taken home.

Unfortunately, the latest marketing trend of 'buy one get one free' (known as 'bogof' in the trade!) encourages extra packaging, for example plastic film around several items such as cans. Children's items also tend to command extra packaging, perhaps to encourage them (or their parents) to buy the goods.

Why pack?

Packaging does, of course, have an important role to play for the following reasons. Packaging:

- is an integral part of the food processing chain, helping manufacturers and consumers transport, store, sell/purchase and use foods more efficiently

 Packaging can enhance the aesthetic appeal of a product but is it always necessary?

- provides protection from external damage and contamination during distribution and keeps the food in good condition throughout its shelf-life
- communicates all necessary information to the consumer about the food, including certain aspects required by law
- is a means of ensuring products are delivered in measured quantities and in the expected condition
- can make food look more attractive, which can promote its use and increase sales.

It is important for a manufacturer to choose carefully when packaging food products. In addition to practical factors such as the type of food product, the choice of packaging will also depend on other **aesthetic** factors. A soft drink, for example, could be sold in a plastic bottle but if the image of this drink is one of an 'upmarket' beverage, a glass bottle may be more appropriate.

Packaging materials

Packing in layers

Packaging used for food products can be divided into three groups:

Primary packaging – the layer that contains the food product, for example a plastic yoghurt carton

Secondary packaging – used when several food products are packed together, for example a cardboard sleeve that holds four yoghurt pots together

Transit packaging – for transporting and distributing large quantities of a food product to retailers, for example many packs of four yoghurts are placed in large containers, usually cardboard boxes, to help with the handling, storage and transportation of the goods.

 Glass bottles are an example of primary packaging.

Glass

Glass has been used as a form of packaging for centuries. Although it is breakable and heavy to transport, these disadvantages are often felt to be outweighed by its ability to be recycled. Glass is easy to wash and sterilize, so it can be recycled many times. It does not affect or react with its contents and it can be clear so consumers can see what they are buying. It can also be made into different shapes and sizes. From the manufacturer's point of view, glass is relatively cheap to produce because it can be made quickly using a highly automated production line (a system that uses machines to carry out tasks automatically). Glass can withstand high temperatures, so it is suitable for use with products that are to be processed by sterilization and preservation, such as jams and pickles. Glass is useful for fizzy drinks because it can resist the internal pressure created by the gas.

Metal

Steel or aluminium cans are used to preserve and contain a whole range of foods, from fruit to frankfurters. Metal is also used to create foil containers, lids and sheets, and metallic finishes are sometimes applied to other materials such as plastics.

Steel cans have to be coated with a layer of tin to prevent the steel from rusting and they do not have 'ring-pulls' because these are easier to make in aluminium. As steel contains more than one metal it is more difficult to recycle. Aluminium, on the other hand, is a strong, lightweight material that is expensive to produce so it is important that it is recycled. Cans are either made from one continuous piece of metal or they are made with a seam. They can withstand high temperatures, and canned food has a shelf-life of many months. Aluminium foil trays and containers have the advantage of being pliable and they can be reused as well as recycled.

Paper

Cardboard and paper are made from cellulose (plant material) and wood pulp. These are natural materials so it is important that all packaging made from them is recycled. Paper and card packaging often has additional layers in order to improve its strength. Plastic or wax coatings are used on card containers and corrugated cardboard is often used for boxes to make them better insulators. Many food products now have cardboard sleeves on which labelling information can be displayed.

Plastic

Plastic first became popular as a food packaging material in the 1960s. It has the advantages of being reasonably cheap and easy to produce, very versatile and extremely lightweight. However, some plastics are felt to be unsuitable for use due to the presence of certain chemicals which can **leach out** into foods, particularly those high in fats.

Most food packaging is thermoplastic, which means it becomes soft on heating and hardens once cool. The advantage of this is that it can be shaped while soft and will stay in that shape unless it is reheated. A variety of different plastics are used for packaging food and are known by abbreviations:

- PP (polypropylene) is used as a clear film or is moulded to produce a rigid container.
- PET (polyester) is also used as a film or for moulding into containers but as it can withstand very high temperatures it can be

used for products that need to be reheated in a microwave.
- PVC (polyvinylchloride) is only used for a limited amount of food packaging due to its possible toxicity in combination with some foods. It is heat resistant and **permeable** to gas and water.
- PS (polystyrene) is used when food needs extra protection. It is a good insulator, too, so it is often used for takeaway food such as burgers.

 Look out for recycling symbols on food packaging.

MAP

Preserving packaging

Preservation helps to delay food spoilage. Packaging enables food to be protected from external damage. **Modified atmosphere packaging (MAP)** provides a way of preserving food through the process of packaging and is sometimes referred to as a shelf-life extension technique.

MAP is packaging that contains food in an atmosphere that is different to the Earth's normal atmosphere (the air we breathe). MAP usually involves the use of three gases: carbon dioxide, nitrogen and oxygen. Different foods are packaged with different combinations and quantities of these gases, depending on the food type.

The Earth's atmosphere

- Nitrogen (N) 78.10%
- Oxygen (O_2) 20.96%
- Carbon dioxide (CO_2) 0.34%
- plus trace inert gases (gases that do not normally react with other materials) and water vapour.

Extending shelf-life

The introduction of MAP techniques has meant that the shelf-life of various products can be extended by between 50 and 500 per cent. This is a bonus for consumers and retailers because waste is minimized. Retailers can also be more flexible when restocking and ordering their goods. In addition, there is less need for the artificial preservatives that are so unpopular with consumers.

How does it work?

Of course, no food product can last forever. Food spoilage is a natural phenomenon but the rate at which different foods decay depends on the type of food and the conditions in which it is kept. Fresh meat and fish and dairy products such as milk, cheese and cream are all regarded as highly perishable. This means they have a relatively short shelf-life.

The fresh meat sold in a supermarket may be packaged using a MAP technique. This enables it to stay on the shelf for longer both in the shop and at home. A second advantage is that the colour of the meat is maintained for longer. The appearance of food is very important to consumers and it is also a good indicator of quality. MAP can involve a gas mixture of between 60 and 80 per cent oxygen to ensure the meat keeps its bright red colour. This does not mean that the deterioration is being disguised but that the process of decay is delayed. The carbon dioxide also present in the gas mix inhibits bacterial growth.

MAP gas

Carbon dioxide inhibits the growth of most aerobic (respire with oxygen) bacteria and moulds. However, CO_2 is absorbed by fats and water, so if the level is too high the flavour of the food may become impaired or it may lose moisture, causing the packaging to collapse. A minimum of 20 per cent CO_2 is recommended. Nitrogen is used to exclude air, particularly oxygen, and to help prevent the collapse of the packaging. Controlled quantities of oxygen are required to maintain a natural colour, to allow the respiration of natural products (such as fruit and vegetables)

Modified atmosphere packaging is now used to package a wide range of products.

and to prevent the growth of anaerobic organisms (that can respire without oxygen).

MAP materials

A range of different materials is used for the packaging of MAP products. The materials are often used together in layers. These include polyester (PET), nylon, polyvinylidene chloride (PVdC) and ethylene vinyl alcohol copolymer (EVOH). The materials must prevent the gases being lost and act as a barrier to water vapour to prevent the food from drying out. The packaging must also withstand the heat often used in **hermetic sealing** and it may need to be transparent so that the consumer can see what is inside. An anti-mist coating is sometimes applied to transparent materials to prevent water droplets forming on the inside of the packet.

MAP foods

Modified atmosphere packaging involves the use of a variety of materials, different combinations of gases and a range of methods in applying the packaging. This diversity means that MAP techniques can be applied to many different types of foods, such as:

- raw meat, offal, poultry, game (for example pheasant), fish and seafood
- cooked and cured meat (for example bacon), poultry, game, fish and seafood
- **cookchill** and ready-meals
- fresh pasta
- cheeses (soft, hard and grated)
- bakery products
- dried foods
- cooked vegetables, fresh fruit and vegetables
- liquid food (for example soup), beverages, carbonated soft drinks.

Products packaged using MAP techniques tend to be more expensive and, of course, the additional packaging means they are not very friendly towards the environment.

Food labels

Label law

It may seem obvious that manufacturers label food products because consumers need to know what they are buying. However, exactly what is put on a food label and how it is worded is carefully controlled in the UK by the Food Labelling Regulations, 1996. These regulations apply to all food for human consumption (except natural mineral waters, which have their own regulations). However, detailed labelling does not apply to certain foods, including honey, hens' eggs, cocoa and chocolate products and some sugar products.

Information that needs to appear on food products must be:
• on the packaging, or
• on a label attached to the pack, or
• on a label that is clearly visible through the packaging.

All food products requiring detailed labelling must be marked as shown below.

Date marks

Use-by dates are shown on highly perishable foods that could be a safety risk if kept or eaten beyond this date. Foods labelled with these dates include fresh meat, fish and cheese. Best-before dates are usually found on foods that can be kept longer than a few days and, if kept or eaten beyond this date, may not be dangerous to health, although they will not be at their best. Foods labelled with these dates include breakfast cereals, biscuits and canned foods.

Labelling on food products is strictly regulated in the UK.

an appropriate label to show shelf-life, for example 'best before' or 'use by'

the name or business name and the address or registration office of the manufacturer, packer or seller established within the EU

any special storage conditions or conditions of use

weight or volume of the contents

instructions for use (if it would be difficult for the consumer to use the food without this information)

Use by 10. 10. 11

Yogpot Ltd
London

Made in England

KEEP REFRIGERATED USE WITHIN 3 DAYS OF OPENING

Extra mild with Bio cultures

NATURAL SET YOGHURT

500g

Made from whole milk and Bio cultures: lactobacilius acidophilus; bifidobacterium longum; streploccus thermophilus no added ingredients

details of the place of origin of the food (if failure to give such information could mislead the consumer about its true origin)

an accurate name

a list of ingredients

Food labels provide information about the product and can include cooking instructions.

Give it a name

In many 'design and make it' activities at school, students are asked to come up with a suitable name for their new food product. In fact, even the naming of food is subject to labelling regulations. Food names are divided into three categories:

1   Names prescribed by law. For example, the species of a fish must be stated, for example plaice.
2   Names that are customary. This is a name that is accepted by consumers, for example Yorkshire Pudding.
3   Names that are not prescribed by law and are not customary names. These names must be chosen so that the consumer gets a sense of the product's 'true nature', meaning an accurate description of the food's main characteristics. In the case of a product name like Mars® bar, the name is followed by 'milk chocolate with soft nougat and caramel centre'.

Do not mislead

Under the Food Labelling Regulations 1996, manufacturers are restricted when making claims about their food products. Claims must not be made in the labelling or advertising of a food unless they fit the guidelines. Even a claim that is implied (rather than being explicit) is not acceptable. Claims might relate to nutrients such as **cholesterol**, protein, vitamins, minerals, energy or the slimming properties of a food. Many 'slimmer's products' have a statement saying they can only help to reduce weight when eaten as part of a **calorie**-controlled diet.

Labelling nutrients

Nutritional labelling refers to any information appearing on a label that relates to any of the following: energy value, protein, carbohydrate, fat, fibre, sodium, vitamins or minerals. However, manufacturers are only allowed to include values for vitamins and minerals if the content is a 'significant amount' (15 per cent of the recommended daily allowance supplied by 100 grams or 100 milliletres, or per package for single portions).

A nutrition claim is any statement, suggestion or implication in the labelling (or advertising) of a food that mentions the nutritional properties in relation to the energy and/or nutrients it does or does not provide, or that says it provides them in a higher or lower quantity than usual. Nutritional labelling is optional, unless a nutrition claim is being made.

Kellogg's packaging – case study

A healthy start

The food company Kellogg's started life at the end of the 19th century when an American physician called Dr John Harvey Kellogg wanted to develop an easy-to-digest breakfast for his patients. This idea was so successful that by 1924 Kellogg's Cornflakes™ and All-Bran were being supplied to UK consumers from the United States.

Pulling power

According to Kellogg's, when it comes to packaging, the packet is probably the most important tool in the 'marketing mix' (that is, all aspects involved in marketing a product from advertising to free samples). It is the manufacturer's opportunity to influence consumers and, hopefully, to persuade them to buy their own brand rather than a competitor's. It has been shown in surveys in America that 70 per cent of sales in supermarkets are impulse purchases, so the pulling power of the packet is very real!

Costing and testing

One important consideration when researching a packaging design is the budget. The launch of a new product is likely to afford a higher budget than if an existing design is just to undergo small changes. A new packet can be tested in many ways, for example to test the shape, design appeal and product name.

Define your market

All products need to be produced and advertised to a **consumer target group**. For example, Kellogg's Ricicles are aimed at the up-to-seven-year age group (the majority of Rice Krispies eaters are under twelve years whereas cornflakes are regarded as a family product with no specific age category). The first step in packaging design is to define the market, for example is it for adults, teenagers or all the family? Is it a specialized product for a particular section of consumers? This information is usually obtained by carrying out thorough consumer research.

Choose your material

The next consideration is the material for the packaging. There is a range of materials to choose from (see pages 32–35) and the decision will be influenced by many factors. Kellogg's suggest these factors might include:
1 the shelf-life required
2 the retail selling price (price at which the item is sold to the consumer)
3 the defined market
4 product protection
5 trade custom (competitive products).

 The way food products are packaged can influence a consumer's decision about their purchase.

Kellogg's have expanded their range of breakfast products in order to meet the needs of different consumer groups.

Trade custom is a new consideration that has come about due to technological advances and the increase in the competitive retail world. Many products can be associated with a traditional type of packaging, for example bread was always wrapped in wax paper but now can be found in cellophane or polyethene.

Kellogg's believe that in a highly competitive situation it may be desirable to fly in the face of trade custom and choose a novel type of packaging that gives you the edge over competitors. However, it is essential that the new packaging is superior to the established type.

Product quantity

The minimum quantity that can be packed is the smallest amount needed by the consumer. The maximum quantity is limited by the cost and product's shelf-life. Two sizes could be produced in order to satisfy a wide range of consumers.

Packaging shape

The shape of a packet may be influenced by the type of packaging machinery available or the shape of the product itself. However, during the development of many products, especially those aimed at children, there is the freedom to experiment with new, eye-catching packs. Kellogg's recommends that the following factors should be considered when thinking about shape:

1   Does the pack include a broad face on the shelves to get maximum exposure?
2   Will it stack well to get the most stock possible on display?
3   If points 1 and 2 are satisfied, will it suit the consumer when it is put to use?
4   Does it have an after-use?
5   Does it have novelty?

When designing packaging, Kellogg's advise having the complete range of products available, including those of the competitors; to use colour illustration and lettering to attract consumers but avoid too much detail or too many gimmicks; and to try out the new design in a store to see how well it works.

AIDA
Package design should fulfil the following criteria:
A – attract Attention
I – create Interest
D – stimulate Desire
A – translate desire into Action

New developments

Population explosion

The population of the UK increased by half between 1901 and 1996. In 2006 the total population for the UK was 60.58 million. This is a huge number of people, all of whom are demanding food on a daily basis. If food and drink were wanted purely to satisfy hunger and thirst, the task perhaps would not be so onerous. But people are insisting on products that meet a whole range of demands, including low cost, high quality, variety, **aesthetic** appeal and easy preparation and cooking. These consumer demands are behind the current drive to use technology that can satisfy the culinary demands of the nation.

Food processing

The food industry uses technology in a variety of ways. Sometimes it is just used to speed up a basic process such as rapidly washing and peeling vegetables that would otherwise have to be prepared by hand. But new techniques have also been developed in order to offer consumers alternative ways to eat, for example by producing chips that can be cooked in the oven. Such food processing includes any action that changes or converts raw plant or animal products into safe, edible and palatable items of food. It also enables the shelf-life of many foods to be extended. In reality, it is unlikely that the needs of today's massive population could be met without the use of food-processing techniques and, without it, we would certainly enjoy far less variety in our diet.

Food processing is not just about **splicing genes** and bombarding foods with **additives**. Most of the foods we buy today have undergone some form of processing, such as the pasteurization of milk or the drying of grapes to form sultanas. For many consumers,

 Today's massive population means the demand for food is greater than ever.

the worry over food processing is not due to its existence but more to do with their lack of knowledge about exactly what is going on in the food industry. The BSE (bovine spongiform encephalalopathy) crisis and other recent food scares have influenced consumers' attitudes towards food products and have seriously affected the food industry, as well as the farming industry, as sales of certain products have fallen.

Food Standards Agency

In April 2000 the UK government set up the Food Standards Agency and gave it the task of raising the standards of food in the UK. It is an independent agency and is run by people with expertise in food safety. It works for consumers in order to:

> 'protect public health from risks which may arise in connection with the consumption of food, and otherwise to protect the interests of consumers in relation to food'.

The Agency has to report its findings to the government's health ministers but it can also publish any advice it gives to the government. Consumers can contact the Agency if they have any specific concerns over a food matter.

Consumer power

Consumer groups have become increasingly concerned about the way foods high in fat, sugar and salt are constantly being advertised during children's television. So much so, that the Food Standards Agency has now published a report stating the serious implications for the long-term health of children. This includes them being at greater risk of heart disease, cancer and diabetes in adult life. The Agency now recommends a code of practice to be drawn up with the food industry, focusing on

The Food Standards Agency was set up to:
- provide advice and information to the public and to the government on food safety from farm to fork, nutrition and diet
- protect consumers through effective enforcement and monitoring
- support consumer choice through promoting accurate and meaningful labelling.

most of the foods aimed at children, such as sweets, snack foods and soft drinks.

Research by the Food Standards Agency has also highlighted consumer concern over food labelling. One of the main issues raised by consumers in a 2006 study was the placement of information on packaging. If labelling could be standardised, then it would be easier for shoppers to find what they were looking for; they would know exactly where to look on packaging for particular information. Logos were thought to be useful in that they are instantly recognisable. Descriptions of the food as well as signposts such as calorie content and low fat indicators were seen to be very important.

Genetically modified (GM) ingredients also proved to be an area of interest for many consumers. As a result, the Food Standards Agency want changes to European food labelling and tighter control on claims about GM ingredients. The Agency also hopes to clear up the confusion for consumers over health claims such as 'low-fat', and 'fat-free'.

Resources

Books

Dictionary of Food Science and Nutrition (A & C Black, 2006)

Food Safety, Victoria Sherrow (Chelsea House Publishers, 2007)

GCSE D&T Food Technology: Complete Revision and Practice, Richard Parsons (Coordination Group Publications, 2005)

GCSE Design and Technology for AQA: Food Technology Student Book, Lesley Woods (Heinemann Educational Publishers, 2005)

Making Healthy Food Choices (series) (Heinemann Library, 2006)

Oxford Dictionary of Food and Nutrition (2nd edition), David A. Bender (Oxford University Press, 2005)

Websites

www.b-eat.co.uk
beat is a UK-based eating disorder charity that provides telephone helplines, publications, training and runs a national network of self-help groups.

www.foodstandards.gov.uk
The Government's information website for the Food Standards Agency contains details of their aims, research, committees, regulations, and press releases. It also addresses topical issues such as food labelling and packaging.

www.eatwell.gov.uk
This site provides the latest news from the Government's Food Standards Agency relating to food and health. Topics include healthy diet, keeping food safe, food labels and health issues.

www.bbc.co.uk/health/healthy_living/nutrition
This site provides lots of information about different foods, dietary requirements and the needs of people at various stages of life.

www.nutrition.org.uk
A charity-run organization that aims to promote the well-being of society by providing information about the relationship between diet, physical activity and health.

www.foe.co.uk
Friends of the Earth is an environmental campaigning organization that tackles issues such as climate change, recycling and genetically modified foods.

Contacts

The Vegan Society
Donald Watson House
21 Hylton Street
Hockley
Birmingham B18 6HJ
www.vegansociety.com
The society promotes ways of living that it believes 'benefit people, animals and the environment'. Information, publications and further links can be found on their website.

Coeliac UK
Suites A–D
Octagon Court
High Wycombe
Bucks HP11 2HS
www.coeliac.co.uk
Provides information about coeliac disease.

Diabetes UK
Central Office
Macleod House
10 Parkway
London NW1 7AA
www.diabetes.org.uk
Offers information and leaflets about diabetes.

SNAGS – School Nutrition Action Groups
Health Education Trust
18 High Street
Broom
Alcester
Worcs B50 4HJ
Tel: 01789 773915
The aim of SNAGS is to increase the uptake of a healthier diet by supporting education and health professionals to improve the range of food and drink provided in their schools.

Place to visit

The Museum of Brands, Packaging and Advertising
2 Colville Mews
Lonsdale Road
Notting Hill
London W11 2AR
www.museumofbrands.com
Two hundred years of consumerism are reflected through packaging, design, brand development and poster and television advertising from the collection of Robert Opie. The museum presents a fascinating insight into the British way of life over the past hundred years.

Glossary

additives   something that is not usually used as a food but is added during the production of a food, either to aid production or to enhance the product in some way (for example appearance, texture)

aesthetic   relates to the beauty or artistic nature of something, such as a creatively arranged plate of food

ambient   refers to a temperature. Ambient foods are found on supermarket shelves and include tinned products, UHT products and dried products.

amino acids   proteins are made up of simpler substances called amino acids, some of which are essential in the growth and development of our bodies. Amino acid molecules are joined together to form long chains.

anaphylactic shock   rare but life-threatening allergic reaction. It occurs in people with an extreme sensitivity to a particular substance (allergen). The sufferer must be given an injection of adrenaline as soon as possible.

calorie   measurement of energy used in nutrition. Units of 1000 calories are written as calories or kilocalories (kcals). Nutritionists today often use kilojoule and megajoule.
1 calorie = 4.18 joules; 1 kJ = 1,000 joules;
1 MJ = 1,000 kilojoules.

carbon emissions   gases, including carbon dioxide, released into the atmosphere, which are believed to contribute to the effect of global warming by trapping the sun's energy

cholesterol   fatty substance naturally present in the body

consumer target group   group of consumers being targeted when marketing a product. The group could be a certain age range (for example babies) or a type of consumer (for example vegetarian).

cookchill   food products that are rapidly chilled immediately after cooking, and then transported and stored at a chilled temperature until they are reheated by the consumer

coronary heart disease   when the blood (and therefore oxygen) supply to a part of the heart is gradually impeded by a narrowing of the vessels supplying the heart. It is caused by fatty substances, including cholesterol.

disposable income   money people may have available to them after they have paid for essential items

ester   chemical name for compounds formed from an acid and an alcohol

fasting   when food is not eaten, for example for religious reasons such as during Ramadam.

fortified   fortified foods and drinks have had nutrients added during processing. Fortified foods include breakfast cereals that have had vitamins and minerals added. These nutrients have to be included on the ingredients list.

genetic   to do with genes that affect heredity

genetically modified   ingredients that have had genes moved or transplanted from another plant or animal in order to improve a characteristic such as colour or texture

hermetic seal   a closure in packaging that prevents food from being contaminated by the environment. It is created using heat and/or pressure.

importation systems   methods used to buy in and transport foods from one country to another

leach out   to move out of one substance and into another; for example vitamins leach out of vegetables and into the cooking water when they are boiled in too much water for too long

modified atmosphere packaging (MAP) packaging technology in which the atmosphere inside a container is altered to extend the shelf-life of the product but retain all the food's natural characteristics (such as its colour)

monosaccharides   simple sugars containing one saccharide unit. When joined together they form disaccharides and polysaccharides. All of these sugars are carbohydrates.

non-starch polysaccharide (NSP)   complex carbohydrates found in foods other than starches; also called fibre or dietary fibre. NSPs may be divided into insoluble (found in wheat, maize, rice) and soluble (found in oats, beans, rye). Vegetables and fruit usually contain both types.

novel protein   protein food that has been developed from new sources; for example, vegetarian protein foods produced from micro-organisms, fungi and algae

patent   form of registration showing that a person owns the sole right to a product or process

pathological   causing disease, for example a pathogenic bacteria can cause food poisoning

permeable   describes an item that will allow substances, such as a gas or a liquid, to pass through it

psychological   in the mind; for example, if a food was eaten just before a person was ill, the person may then associate the food with illness and have an adverse reaction when eating it; there is no physical cause, as in the case of a food allergy or intolerance

risk factor   something that contributes to the risk of a disease or illness. For example, smoking, lack of exercise, high blood pressure and a high fat diet are all risk factors for coronary heart disease.

saturated fat   saturated fats have a higher proportion of saturated fatty acids than unsaturated fatty acids. Their structure means that each carbon chain has its full complement of hydrogen atoms (it is saturated with them). These fats are mainly from animal sources and are solid at room temperature (butter, lard, fat on meat, or meat fat).

smart foods   foods that have been developed through the invention of new or improved processes

splicing genes   altering genes during food production by making a copy of a desirable gene and putting it into another plant or animal

staple   principal food, particularly of a region or country, usually high in carbohydrate; for example rice is a staple food of China

textured vegetable protein (TVP)   vegetable protein usually made to resemble meat

trimester   three-monthly period into which a full-term pregnancy is divided. The first three months are called the first trimester, months four to six are the second trimester and the final trimester consists of the seventh, eighth and ninth months.

Index

additives 12, 13, 42
advertising 9, 43
alcohol 15, 28
allergies 12–13
amino acids 11
anaphylactic shock 12
anorexia nervosa 20, 21

babies and children 9, 13, 14–15, 27, 28–9, 43
bagels 19
barbecues 17
Benecol 31
best-before/use-by dates 38
bingeing 20
body fat 22
body mass index (BMI) 22, 23
BSE 10, 43
bulimia nervosa 20–1

calories/kilojoules 15, 19, 23, 28, 39
cans 34–5
carbohydrates 14, 24, 25
carbon emissions, reducing 5
children see babies and children
Children's Food Campaign 9
cholesterol 31, 39
coeliac disease 12–13
consumer target groups 8–9, 40
convenience foods 5, 6, 30
cooking methods 17
coronary heart disease 10, 22, 24, 31, 43

datemarks 38
diabetes 14–15, 22, 43
dietary customs 16–17
dietary guidelines 24–5, 26–7
Dietary Reference Values (DRVs) 24–5

eating disorders 20–1
eating habits and trends 6–7
endorphins 21
environmental issues 5, 7, 32–3
exercise 22, 23, 29

Fairtrade food schemes 7
fast food 18–19, 22

fasting 16, 20
fats 19, 22, 24, 25, 31
    saturated fats 10, 14, 24, 25, 26, 29
five-a-day campaign (fruits and vegetables) 25
folic acid 28
food intolerance 12
food safety 10, 43
food spoilage 36
Food Standards Agency 24, 43
functional foods 31

genetically modified foods 6, 43
glass (packaging) 34
glucose 14
gluten 12, 13
grazing 6, 7

health claims 31, 39, 43
health issues 9, 10, 12, 13, 14–15, 20–3, 24, 31, 43
healthy eating 15, 24–7
hyperactivity 13

insulin 14

junk food 9

Kellogg's 40–1
kitchen gadgets 30

labelling 13, 31, 35, 38–9, 43

Marks and Spencer 26–7
metal (packaging) 34–5
microwave cooking 30
modified atmosphere packaging (MAP) 5, 36–7
monosaccharides 14
multicultural eating habits 9, 16–17

non-starch polysaccharide (NSP) 10, 14, 24, 31
nutrients 11, 24, 39

obesity 22–3
older people 9
online shopping 4–5
organic foods 6

packaging 5, 30, 32–7, 40–1
    costs 32
    design 40–1
    function 33
    layered 34
    materials 34–5, 37, 40
    modified atmosphere packaging (MAP) 5, 36–7
    recycling 33, 35
paper (packaging) 35
pets, overweight 23
pizzas 30
plastic (packaging) 35
population growth 42
pregnancy 28
preservatives 36
processed foods 5, 13, 30, 42–3
protein 11, 25
    novel proteins 11

Quorn™ 11

ready-meals 5, 8, 11, 30

salt 9, 14, 16, 24, 26, 29
sandwiches 18–19, 26
seasonal foods 7
shelf-life 5, 36, 40, 42
shopping for food 4–5, 6
single households 8, 9, 16
slimming diets 23, 39
smart foods 31
staple foods 16, 17
stomach stapling 23
sugary products 9, 14, 15, 29
supermarkets/superstores 4, 5, 40
sushi 19

textured vegetable protein (TVP) 10, 11
tooth decay 21, 28

value-added products 30, 31
vegans 10
vegetarians 9, 10–11, 16, 17

weight control 15, 23, 39
women 8, 20, 21, 28

young people 9